# JOURNAL

## TODAY'S LIGHT BIBLE

The Livingstone Corporation produced this journal exclusively for
Concordia Publishing House. Project staff includes James C. Galvin,
Jonathan Farrar. Cover and interior design by Paetzold Design.

ISBN#: 0-570-00535-3

# JOURNAL

## Capture the Memories of Your Time With God

# TODAY'S
# LIGHT
### BIBLE

CPH.
SAINT LOUIS

# Keeping A Spiritual Journal

*Is your Bible reading interactive? Perhaps you own a computer Bible with interactive features. But even if you do, that's not what I mean by asking this question. Instead I'm talking about what happens between you and your Lord as you read His Word.*

*You see, the Holy Spirit intends that our Scripture reading become more and more a dialog. As we read, we need to ask questions—questions like these:*
- Where am I in this text, Lord?
- What sins would you like to confront, forgive, and empower me to overcome?
- What comfort would you like to give me? What encouragement?

*As we read, we also need to tell God what is on our hearts, things like these:*
- There is no God like You, Lord!
- I'm not sure I understand this truth, dear Jesus.
- I see Your promise here, Lord, but it doesn't seem to work out in my life. Help me understand it better.

God does speak to us. The Holy Scripture is His Word to the whole human race. But it is also His personal letter of love to you, His child, and an individual Christian believer. Journaling is a good way to realize and to capitalize on this truth.

# Spiritual Journaling—Law and Gospel

Perhaps you've kept a spiritual journal over the years. If so, by now you've probably discovered what an enriching experience it can be. But even if you have no interest in journaling, you can deepen your devotional life by keeping two key doctrines in mind as you study Scripture—Law and Gospel. Journaling with these doctrines in mind will make it possible for you to apply God's Word to your own life more personally and powerfully than even before. Listen to what Martin Luther said about that: *"If some passage is obscure I consider whether it treats of grace or of Law, whether wrath or the forgiveness of sin [is contained in it], and with which of these it agrees better. By this procedure I have often understood the most obscure passages. Either the Law or the Gospel has made them meaningful, for God divides His teaching into Law and Gospel."*

*As you journal, think about a particular Scriptural text. Ask yourself these questions:*

- Does this passage reveal sin in my life?
- Or does it show me my Savior?
- Does it make demands of me?
- Or does it show me what God has already done for me in Christ?

When you identify sin in your heart and life, confess it. Receive the assurance that comes from God's forgiving love through Christ's cross. Then let yourself look at what God's Law requires in a new light. Look at it as a possibility He holds out to you for your joy as His redeemed and righteous person. We no longer *must* obey, we *can*! We get to obey! His Spirit works both the desire and the power for new obedience in our hearts (Philippians 2:13).

By God's grace, our new life in Christ produces in us a new lifestyle. You can write it down in your journal. But better yet, you can live it out in your life as God's Spirit works in you.

# SPIRITUAL JOURNALING—PRAYING THE SCRIPTURES

Another benefit of journaling as you read the Scriptures comes as you reread what you have written and pray about it. You may want to use the ACTS acronym some days as you conclude your devotional time. You may even want to use the ACTS acronym as you organize your thoughts in your journal. Touch on each of these aspects of prayer:

**ADORATION**—Begin with words of praise to God for His goodness, grace, and mercy as the day's Scripture reading reveals those attributes in specific ways.

**CONFESSION**—Acknowledge the particular sinful attitudes, actions, thoughts, or words that the Holy Spirit helps you recognize in yourself as you read along. Ask for His forgiveness, for the assurance of His ongoing love, and for power to resist the temptation to repeat those sins in the future.

**THANKSGIVING**—This differs from *praise* in that praise mainly involves *who God is*, and thanks mainly responds to *what He has done*. Ask yourself, "What does God promise me in this text? What has He done for me in history as revealed in this text? What benefits of living as His child does this text bring to mind?" Then write out your words of thanksgiving.

**SUPPLICATION**—This word comes from a root word meaning "to bend" as in "to bend the knee," and evokes the picture of a servant approaching his or her king to ask favors. We come to the Lord in humble trust to ask for His help for others and for ourselves. Base your requests on the promises and precedents given in the reading you have done. If you write out your requests and date them, you will have a record that will reveal over time all the Lord's many answers to your prayers.

From time to time read back over your journal entries. Review what you've learned about yourself and especially about your Savior and His abiding grace and love.

# Spiritual Journaling—the Nuts and Bolts

1.  Pray your way through the process. Our Lord Jesus has promised that the Holy Spirit will be our teacher as we approach His Word (John 14:25–26). Ask for His help!

2.  Don't strive for eloquent observations or creative conclusions. You need not even strive for pious thoughts as you journal. But do make your comments honest. Share the thoughts and questions and desires of your heart with your heavenly Father. Remember that He already knows what we feel and need. When we tell Him honestly, He holds out to us His promises and pardon.

3.  You need not write lengthy treatises. In fact, you need not write in your journal every day. Aim at a few sentences once or twice a week at first. With experience you will come to sense texts from Scripture that will become clearer as you think about them in writing.

4. Here is a list of questions that you can use as thought starters. You may want to substitute your own questions as you approach some texts, or ignore them altogether. In any case, this is your journal. Do what will benefit you most.

- Where does God's Law confront any aspect of your life in this text? Where does the Gospel bring you comfort?

- What parts of this text are amazing to you? Did the passage surprise you in any way?

- Based on this text, develop a prayer plan. What praises, thanksgivings, confessions, and requests do you want to include in your prayer time today?

- Where do you see yourself in today's reading? Where do you see God's forgiving love in Jesus?

- What key truths have you seen in God's Word today? Where else have you encountered these truths? What impact do they make in your life?

- As you read today, what questions came to mind? What do you want to ask Jesus about them?

- In what ways does this text increase your confidence in your Savior's love?

- If you could sit down with the human author of today's Scripture, what would you like to ask him?

- If you could underline only one verse from today's text, which would you choose? Why?

- Which parts of today's reading would you like to share with someone? Who? Why? How might you do this?

*For your convenience, we have also listed these questions on the bottom of the pages in this journal. Use them to help stimulate your thinking.*

*Where does God's Law confront any aspect of your life in this text?*
*Where does the Gospel bring you comfort?*

*Journal*

What parts of this text are amazing to you?
Did the passage surprise you in any way?

*Based on this text, develop a prayer plan. What praises, thanksgivings, confessions, and requests do you want to include in your prayer time today?*

*Where do you see yourself in today's reading? Where do you see God's forgiving love in Jesus?*

*What key truths have you seen in God's Word today? Where else have you
encountered these truths? What impact do they make in your life?*

*As you read today, what questions came to mind?*
*What do you want to ask Jesus about them?*

*In what ways does this text increase your confidence in your Savior's love?*

*If you could sit down with the human author of today's Scripture,
what would you like to ask him?*

*If you could underline only one verse from today's text,*
*which would you choose? Why?*

*Which parts of today's reading would you like to share with someone?*
*Who? Why? How might you do this?*

*Where does God's Law confront any aspect of your life in this text?*
*Where does the Gospel bring you comfort?*

*What parts of this text are amazing to you?*
*Did the passage surprise you in any way?*

*Based on this text, develop a prayer plan. What praises, thanksgivings, confessions, and requests do you want to include in your prayer time today?*

*Where do you see yourself in today's reading? Where do you see God's forgiving love in Jesus?*

*What key truths have you seen in God's Word today? Where else have you encountered these truths? What impact do they make in your life?*

*As you read today, what questions came to mind?*
*What do you want to ask Jesus about them?*

*In what ways does this text increase your confidence in your Savior's love?*

*If you could sit down with the human author of today's Scripture,*
*what would you like to ask him?*

*If you could underline only one verse from today's text,
which would you choose? Why?*

*J o u r n a l*

Which parts of today's reading would you like to share with someone?
Who? Why? How might you do this?

*Where does God's Law confront any aspect of your life in this text?*
*Where does the Gospel bring you comfort?*

*What parts of this text are amazing to you?*
*Did the passage surprise you in any way?*

*Based on this text, develop a prayer plan. What praises, thanksgivings, confessions, and requests do you want to include in your prayer time today?*

*Where do you see yourself in today's reading? Where do you see God's forgiving love in Jesus?*

*What key truths have you seen in God's Word today? Where else have you encountered these truths? What impact do they make in your life?*

*As you read today, what questions came to mind?*
*What do you want to ask Jesus about them?*

*In what ways does this text increase your confidence in your Savior's love?*

*If you could sit down with the human author of today's Scripture,
what would you like to ask him?*

*If you could underline only one verse from today's text,
which would you choose? Why?*

*Which parts of today's reading would you like to share with someone?*
*Who? Why? How might you do this?*

*Where does God's Law confront any aspect of your life in this text?*
*Where does the Gospel bring you comfort?*

*What parts of this text are amazing to you?*
*Did the passage surprise you in any way?*

_Based on this text, develop a prayer plan. What praises, thanksgivings, confessions, and requests do you want to include in your prayer time today?_

*Where do you see yourself in today's reading? Where do you see God's forgiving love in Jesus?*

*What key truths have you seen in God's Word today? Where else have you encountered these truths? What impact do they make in your life?*

_As you read today, what questions came to mind?_
_What do you want to ask Jesus about them?_

*In what ways does this text increase your confidence in your Savior's love?*

*Journal*

*If you could sit down with the human author of today's Scripture,
what would you like to ask him?*

*If you could underline only one verse from today's text,*
*which would you choose? Why?*

*Journal*

*Which parts of today's reading would you like to share with someone?*
*Who? Why? How might you do this?*

*Where does God's Law confront any aspect of your life in this text?*
*Where does the Gospel bring you comfort?*

*Journal*

*What parts of this text are amazing to you?*
*Did the passage surprise you in any way?*

_Based on this text, develop a prayer plan. What praises, thanksgivings, confessions, and requests do you want to include in your prayer time today?_

*Where do you see yourself in today's reading? Where do you see
God's forgiving love in Jesus?*

*What key truths have you seen in God's Word today? Where else have you encountered these truths? What impact do they make in your life?*

*Journal*

As you read today, what questions came to mind?
What do you want to ask Jesus about them?

*In what ways does this text increase your confidence in your Savior's love?*

*If you could sit down with the human author of today's Scripture, what would you like to ask him?*

*If you could underline only one verse from today's text,*
*which would you choose? Why?*

*Which parts of today's reading would you like to share with someone?*
*Who? Why? How might you do this?*

*Where does God's Law confront any aspect of your life in this text?*
*Where does the Gospel bring you comfort?*

*What parts of this text are amazing to you?*
*Did the passage surprise you in any way?*

*Based on this text, develop a prayer plan. What praises, thanksgivings, confessions, and requests do you want to include in your prayer time today?*

*Where do you see yourself in today's reading? Where do you see God's forgiving love in Jesus?*

*What key truths have you seen in God's Word today? Where else have you encountered these truths? What impact do they make in your life?*

*As you read today, what questions came to mind?*
*What do you want to ask Jesus about them?*

*In what ways does this text increase your confidence in your
Savior's love?*

*If you could sit down with the human author of today's Scripture,
what would you like to ask him?*

*If you could underline only one verse from today's text,*
*which would you choose? Why?*

*Journal*

*Which parts of today's reading would you like to share with someone?*
*Who? Why? How might you do this?*

*Where does God's Law confront any aspect of your life in this text?*
*Where does the Gospel bring you comfort?*

*Journal*

*What parts of this text are amazing to you?*
*Did the passage surprise you in any way?*

_Based on this text, develop a prayer plan. What praises, thanksgivings, confessions, and requests do you want to include in your prayer time today?_

*Where do you see yourself in today's reading? Where do you see God's forgiving love in Jesus?*

*What key truths have you seen in God's Word today? Where else have you
encountered these truths? What impact do they make in your life?*

*As you read today, what questions came to mind?*
*What do you want to ask Jesus about them?*

*In what ways does this text increase your confidence in your Savior's love?*

*If you could sit down with the human author of today's Scripture,
what would you like to ask him?*

*If you could underline only one verse from today's text,
which would you choose? Why?*

*Which parts of today's reading would you like to share with someone?*
*Who? Why? How might you do this?*

*Where does God's Law confront any aspect of your life in this text?*
*Where does the Gospel bring you comfort?*

What parts of this text are amazing to you?
Did the passage surprise you in any way?

*Based on this text, develop a prayer plan. What praises, thanksgivings, confessions, and requests do you want to include in your prayer time today?*

_Where do you see yourself in today's reading? Where do you see God's forgiving love in Jesus?_

*What key truths have you seen in God's Word today? Where else have you encountered these truths? What impact do they make in your life?*

*Journal*

*As you read today, what questions came to mind?*
*What do you want to ask Jesus about them?*

*In what ways does this text increase your confidence in your Savior's love?*

*Journal*

If you could sit down with the human author of today's Scripture,
what would you like to ask him?

*If you could underline only one verse from today's text,*
*which would you choose? Why?*

*Which parts of today's reading would you like to share with someone?*
*Who? Why? How might you do this?*

*Where does God's Law confront any aspect of your life in this text?*
*Where does the Gospel bring you comfort?*

*J o u r n a l*

What parts of this text are amazing to you?
Did the passage surprise you in any way?

*Based on this text, develop a prayer plan. What praises, thanksgivings, confessions, and requests do you want to include in your prayer time today?*

*Journal*

Where do you see yourself in today's reading? Where do you see
God's forgiving love in Jesus?

*What key truths have you seen in God's Word today? Where else have you encountered these truths? What impact do they make in your life?*

*As you read today, what questions came to mind?*
*What do you want to ask Jesus about them?*

*In what ways does this text increase your confidence in your Savior's love?*

*If you could sit down with the human author of today's Scripture,*
*what would you like to ask him?*

*If you could underline only one verse from today's text,*
*which would you choose? Why?*

*Which parts of today's reading would you like to share with someone?*
*Who? Why? How might you do this?*

*Where does God's Law confront any aspect of your life in this text?*
*Where does the Gospel bring you comfort?*

*What parts of this text are amazing to you?*
*Did the passage surprise you in any way?*

_Based on this text, develop a prayer plan. What praises, thanksgivings, confessions, and requests do you want to include in your prayer time today?_

*Where do you see yourself in today's reading? Where do you see God's forgiving love in Jesus?*

*What key truths have you seen in God's Word today? Where else have you encountered these truths? What impact do they make in your life?*

*Journal*

As you read today, what questions came to mind?
What do you want to ask Jesus about them?

*In what ways does this text increase your confidence in your Savior's love?*

*If you could sit down with the human author of today's Scripture,*
*what would you like to ask him?*

*If you could underline only one verse from today's text,*
*which would you choose? Why?*

*Which parts of today's reading would you like to share with someone?*
*Who? Why? How might you do this?*

*Where does God's Law confront any aspect of your life in this text?*
*Where does the Gospel bring you comfort?*

*What parts of this text are amazing to you?*
*Did the passage surprise you in any way?*

Based on this text, develop a prayer plan. What praises, thanksgivings, confessions, and requests do you want to include in your prayer time today?

*Where do you see yourself in today's reading? Where do you see God's forgiving love in Jesus?*

*What key truths have you seen in God's Word today? Where else have you encountered these truths? What impact do they make in your life?*

*As you read today, what questions came to mind?*
*What do you want to ask Jesus about them?*

*In what ways does this text increase your confidence in your Savior's love?*

*Journal*

If you could sit down with the human author of today's Scripture,
what would you like to ask him?

*If you could underline only one verse from today's text,*
*which would you choose? Why?*

*Which parts of today's reading would you like to share with someone?*
*Who? Why? How might you do this?*

*Where does God's Law confront any aspect of your life in this text?*
*Where does the Gospel bring you comfort?*

*Journal*

What parts of this text are amazing to you?
Did the passage surprise you in any way?

*Based on this text, develop a prayer plan. What praises, thanksgivings, confessions, and requests do you want to include in your prayer time today?*

*Where do you see yourself in today's reading? Where do you see God's forgiving love in Jesus?*

*What key truths have you seen in God's Word today? Where else have you encountered these truths? What impact do they make in your life?*

*As you read today, what questions came to mind?*
*What do you want to ask Jesus about them?*

*In what ways does this text increase your confidence in your Savior's love?*

*If you could sit down with the human author of today's Scripture,*
*what would you like to ask him?*

*If you could underline only one verse from today's text,*
*which would you choose? Why?*

*Which parts of today's reading would you like to share with someone?*
*Who? Why? How might you do this?*

*Where does God's Law confront any aspect of your life in this text?*
*Where does the Gospel bring you comfort?*

*Journal*

What parts of this text are amazing to you?
Did the passage surprise you in any way?

*Based on this text, develop a prayer plan. What praises, thanksgivings, confessions, and requests do you want to include in your prayer time today?*

*Where do you see yourself in today's reading? Where do you see
God's forgiving love in Jesus?*

*What key truths have you seen in God's Word today? Where else have you encountered these truths? What impact do they make in your life?*

*As you read today, what questions came to mind?*
*What do you want to ask Jesus about them?*

*In what ways does this text increase your confidence in your*
*Savior's love?*

*If you could sit down with the human author of today's Scripture,*
*what would you like to ask him?*

*If you could underline only one verse from today's text,*
*which would you choose? Why?*

*Journal*

*Which parts of today's reading would you like to share with someone?*
*Who? Why? How might you do this?*

*Where does God's Law confront any aspect of your life in this text?*
*Where does the Gospel bring you comfort?*

*Journal*

*What parts of this text are amazing to you?*
*Did the passage surprise you in any way?*

*Based on this text, develop a prayer plan. What praises, thanksgivings, confessions, and requests do you want to include in your prayer time today?*

_____
_____
_____
_____
_____
_____
_____
_____
_____
_____
_____
_____
_____
_____
_____
_____
_____
_____
_____
_____
_____
_____

*Where do you see yourself in today's reading? Where do you see
God's forgiving love in Jesus?*

*What key truths have you seen in God's Word today? Where else have you encountered these truths? What impact do they make in your life?*

*Journal*

*As you read today, what questions came to mind?*
*What do you want to ask Jesus about them?*

*In what ways does this text increase your confidence in your Savior's love?*

_If you could sit down with the human author of today's Scripture,_
_what would you like to ask him?_

*If you could underline only one verse from today's text,*
*which would you choose? Why?*

*Which parts of today's reading would you like to share with someone?*
*Who? Why? How might you do this?*

*Where does God's Law confront any aspect of your life in this text?*
*Where does the Gospel bring you comfort?*

*What parts of this text are amazing to you?*
*Did the passage surprise you in any way?*

*Based on this text, develop a prayer plan. What praises, thanksgivings, confessions, and requests do you want to include in your prayer time today?*

*Where do you see yourself in today's reading? Where do you see God's forgiving love in Jesus?*

*What key truths have you seen in God's Word today? Where else have you encountered these truths? What impact do they make in your life?*

*J  o  u  r  n  a  l*

*As you read today, what questions came to mind?*
*What do you want to ask Jesus about them?*

*In what ways does this text increase your confidence in your Savior's love?*

*If you could sit down with the human author of today's Scripture,
what would you like to ask him?*

*If you could underline only one verse from today's text,*
*which would you choose? Why?*

*Which parts of today's reading would you like to share with someone?*
*Who? Why? How might you do this?*

*Where does God's Law confront any aspect of your life in this text?*
*Where does the Gospel bring you comfort?*

*Journal*

*What parts of this text are amazing to you?*
*Did the passage surprise you in any way?*

*Based on this text, develop a prayer plan. What praises, thanksgivings, confessions, and requests do you want to include in your prayer time today?*

*Where do you see yourself in today's reading? Where do you see
God's forgiving love in Jesus?*

*What key truths have you seen in God's Word today? Where else have you encountered these truths? What impact do they make in your life?*

*Journal*

As you read today, what questions came to mind?
What do you want to ask Jesus about them?

*In what ways does this text increase your confidence in your Savior's love?*

*If you could sit down with the human author of today's Scripture,*
*what would you like to ask him?*

*If you could underline only one verse from today's text,*
*which would you choose? Why?*

*Which parts of today's reading would you like to share with someone?*
*Who? Why? How might you do this?*

*Where does God's Law confront any aspect of your life in this text?*
*Where does the Gospel bring you comfort?*

*What parts of this text are amazing to you?*
*Did the passage surprise you in any way?*

*Based on this text, develop a prayer plan. What praises, thanksgivings, confessions, and requests do you want to include in your prayer time today?*

*Where do you see yourself in today's reading? Where do you see God's forgiving love in Jesus?*

*What key truths have you seen in God's Word today? Where else have you encountered these truths? What impact do they make in your life?*

*As you read today, what questions came to mind?*
*What do you want to ask Jesus about them?*

*In what ways does this text increase your confidence in your Savior's love?*

*If you could sit down with the human author of today's Scripture,*
*what would you like to ask him?*

*If you could underline only one verse from today's text,*
*which would you choose? Why?*

*Which parts of today's reading would you like to share with someone?*
*Who? Why? How might you do this?*

*Where does God's Law confront any aspect of your life in this text?*
*Where does the Gospel bring you comfort?*

*Journal*

What parts of this text are amazing to you?
Did the passage surprise you in any way?

*Based on this text, develop a prayer plan. What praises, thanksgivings, confessions, and requests do you want to include in your prayer time today?*

*Where do you see yourself in today's reading? Where do you see God's forgiving love in Jesus?*

*What key truths have you seen in God's Word today? Where else have you encountered these truths? What impact do they make in your life?*

*As you read today, what questions came to mind?*
*What do you want to ask Jesus about them?*

*In what ways does this text increase your confidence in your Savior's love?*

*If you could sit down with the human author of today's Scripture,
what would you like to ask him?*

*If you could underline only one verse from today's text,*
*which would you choose? Why?*

*Journal*

*Which parts of today's reading would you like to share with someone?
Who? Why? How might you do this?*

*Where does God's Law confront any aspect of your life in this text?*
*Where does the Gospel bring you comfort?*

*What parts of this text are amazing to you?*
*Did the passage surprise you in any way?*

*Based on this text, develop a prayer plan. What praises, thanksgivings, confessions, and requests do you want to include in your prayer time today?*

*Where do you see yourself in today's reading? Where do you see
God's forgiving love in Jesus?*

*What key truths have you seen in God's Word today? Where else have you encountered these truths? What impact do they make in your life?*

*As you read today, what questions came to mind?*
*What do you want to ask Jesus about them?*

*In what ways does this text increase your confidence in your Savior's love?*

*If you could sit down with the human author of today's Scripture,*
*what would you like to ask him?*

*If you could underline only one verse from today's text,
which would you choose? Why?*

*J o u r n a l*

Which parts of today's reading would you like to share with someone?
Who? Why? How might you do this?

*Where does God's Law confront any aspect of your life in this text?*
*Where does the Gospel bring you comfort?*

_What parts of this text are amazing to you?_
_Did the passage surprise you in any way?_

*Based on this text, develop a prayer plan. What praises, thanksgivings, confessions, and requests do you want to include in your prayer time today?*

*Where do you see yourself in today's reading? Where do you see God's forgiving love in Jesus?*

*What key truths have you seen in God's Word today? Where else have you encountered these truths? What impact do they make in your life?*

*Journal*

As you read today, what questions came to mind?
What do you want to ask Jesus about them?

*In what ways does this text increase your confidence in your Savior's love?*

*If you could sit down with the human author of today's Scripture,*
*what would you like to ask him?*

*If you could underline only one verse from today's text,
which would you choose? Why?*

*Which parts of today's reading would you like to share with someone?*
*Who? Why? How might you do this?*

*Where does God's Law confront any aspect of your life in this text?*
*Where does the Gospel bring you comfort?*

*Journal*

What parts of this text are amazing to you?
Did the passage surprise you in any way?

*Based on this text, develop a prayer plan. What praises, thanksgivings, confessions, and requests do you want to include in your prayer time today?*

*Journal*

*Where do you see yourself in today's reading? Where do you see God's forgiving love in Jesus?*

*What key truths have you seen in God's Word today? Where else have you encountered these truths? What impact do they make in your life?*

*As you read today, what questions came to mind?*
*What do you want to ask Jesus about them?*

*In what ways does this text increase your confidence in your Savior's love?*

*If you could sit down with the human author of today's Scripture,*
*what would you like to ask him?*

*If you could underline only one verse from today's text,*
*which would you choose? Why?*

*Which parts of today's reading would you like to share with someone?*
*Who? Why? How might you do this?*

*Where does God's Law confront any aspect of your life in this text?*
*Where does the Gospel bring you comfort?*

What parts of this text are amazing to you?
Did the passage surprise you in any way?

*Based on this text, develop a prayer plan. What praises, thanksgivings, confessions, and requests do you want to include in your prayer time today?*

*Where do you see yourself in today's reading? Where do you see God's forgiving love in Jesus?*

*What key truths have you seen in God's Word today? Where else have you encountered these truths? What impact do they make in your life?*

*As you read today, what questions came to mind?*
*What do you want to ask Jesus about them?*

*In what ways does this text increase your confidence in your Savior's love?*

*If you could sit down with the human author of today's Scripture,
what would you like to ask him?*

*If you could underline only one verse from today's text,
which would you choose? Why?*

*Journal*

Which parts of today's reading would you like to share with someone?
Who? Why? How might you do this?

*Where does God's Law confront any aspect of your life in this text?*
*Where does the Gospel bring you comfort?*

*Journal*

What parts of this text are amazing to you?
Did the passage surprise you in any way?

*Based on this text, develop a prayer plan. What praises, thanksgivings, confessions, and requests do you want to include in your prayer time today?*

*Where do you see yourself in today's reading? Where do you see God's forgiving love in Jesus?*

*What key truths have you seen in God's Word today? Where else have you encountered these truths? What impact do they make in your life?*

*As you read today, what questions came to mind?*
*What do you want to ask Jesus about them?*

_In what ways does this text increase your confidence in your
Savior's love?_

*If you could sit down with the human author of today's Scripture,*
*what would you like to ask him?*

*If you could underline only one verse from today's text,
which would you choose? Why?*

*Journal*

*Which parts of today's reading would you like to share with someone?
Who? Why? How might you do this?*

*Where does God's Law confront any aspect of your life in this text?*
*Where does the Gospel bring you comfort?*

*Journal*

What parts of this text are amazing to you?
Did the passage surprise you in any way?

*Based on this text, develop a prayer plan. What praises, thanksgivings, confessions, and requests do you want to include in your prayer time today?*

*Where do you see yourself in today's reading? Where do you see God's forgiving love in Jesus?*

*What key truths have you seen in God's Word today? Where else have you encountered these truths? What impact do they make in your life?*

*As you read today, what questions came to mind?*
*What do you want to ask Jesus about them?*

*In what ways does this text increase your confidence in your Savior's love?*

*If you could sit down with the human author of today's Scripture,
what would you like to ask him?*

*If you could underline only one verse from today's text,*
*which would you choose? Why?*

*Which parts of today's reading would you like to share with someone?*
*Who? Why? How might you do this?*

*Where does God's Law confront any aspect of your life in this text?*
*Where does the Gospel bring you comfort?*

*J  o  u  r  n  a  l*

What parts of this text are amazing to you?
Did the passage surprise you in any way?

*Based on this text, develop a prayer plan. What praises, thanksgivings, confessions, and requests do you want to include in your prayer time today?*

*J  o  u  r  n  a  l*

Where do you see yourself in today's reading? Where do you see
God's forgiving love in Jesus?

*What key truths have you seen in God's Word today? Where else have you encountered these truths? What impact do they make in your life?*

*As you read today, what questions came to mind?*
*What do you want to ask Jesus about them?*

*In what ways does this text increase your confidence in your Savior's love?*

*If you could sit down with the human author of today's Scripture,*
*what would you like to ask him?*

*If you could underline only one verse from today's text,*
*which would you choose? Why?*